page 2

Finch   Kinsman   Hagarth

C000057904

page 2

2   4   1   1   3   2   3   4

1000

page 4

£28 434   £12 895   £18 435   £14 750

100

page 14

$\frac{5}{12}$ $\frac{2}{5}$ $\frac{1}{3}$ $\frac{1}{4}$

10

3400

$\frac{5}{8}$ $\frac{5}{12}$

340

34

page 16

3   5   6   10

Well done!

Good job!

Clever me!

page 22

tariff 1   tariff 2   tariff 3   tariff 4   tariff 1   tariff 2   tariff 3   tariff 4

page 24

Clever me!

page 27

<   <   <

>   >   >

=   >   =

Well done!

Good job!

Leap Ahead Workbook

Maths

Home learning made fun

fun

Menu

1/2   Mushrooms

30%   Ham & pineapple

0.2   Pepperoni

Key Stage 2

igloobooks

Big numbers

Robbie wants to be a professional footballer and he has been researching how much his favourite players earn.

Randles
£14 568 400

Finch
£8 235 938

Kinsman
£8 098 324

Hagarth
£15 408 276

Use the stickers on your sticker sheet to place the footballers' names in order of their wages from lowest to highest.

Lowest ⟶ Highest

When their new contracts are released, their wages change according to how well they have played. Complete the table with their new wages.

player name	wage change	new wages
Randles	£600 000 decrease	
Finch	£70 000 increase	
Kinsman	£450 000 increase	
Hagarth	£9000 decrease	

Below are the wages of two more footballers. Can you insert the missing digit in each wage to show who earns the most? Choose two digits from your sticker sheet. There are several correct answers.

£2 32 ◯ 450 < £2 3 ◯ 3 640

Answers on page 32

Decimal numbers

Robbie and his friends play for a local football team. Their coach gives them fitness trackers to see how far they run during training. The trackers are set to kilometres.

Robbie's tracker shows 8.164 and James' shows 8.4. Robbie tells James, "I've run farthest because my distance has more digits."
Is Robbie correct? What should James say?

....

....

William has accidentally set his to metres (14 003m) so he divides it by 1000 to convert it to kilometres. He says he has run 14.3km. Is he right?

....

At the next training session, they all set their trackers to metres.
Can you divide their distances by 1000 to convert them to kilometres?

Robbie	Jenny	William	Poppy	Connor
12 042m	9802m	10 460m	15 800m	8045m

....

Robbie practises converting more distances but gets muddy fingerprints over the sums. Find the missing numbers on the sticker sheet.

$$1\ 3\ .\ 4\ k\ m\quad \times \quad \underline{\qquad} \quad = \quad 1\ 3\ \ 4\ 0\ 0\ m$$

$$\underline{\qquad}\ c\ m\quad \div\quad 1\ 0\ 0\quad = \quad 3\ 4\ m$$

Answers on page 32

PARENT TIP: Make flashcards with ×10, ×100, ×1000, ÷10, ÷100, ÷1000 and a mixture of whole numbers and decimal numbers, and divide into two piles. Take turns to pick up a flashcard from each pile and carry out the calculation, e.g. [3.41] [× 1000] = 3410. Whoever has the biggest answer wins the round.

3

Rounding numbers

£13 549   £15 049   £14 099   £12 549

Kyle's dad is looking to spend about £13 000 on a new car. Which of the cars at the dealership would round to £13 000 to the nearest thousand?

....

He agrees to buy the red car if the salesman will round it down to the nearest thousand. How much will he pay?

....

The salesman wants to round it down to the nearest hundred. What do you notice about the new price?

....

The salesman has got the new prices for some of the cars in a muddle. His manager gives him a clue about each price:

"The price on the red car rounds to £14 800 when rounded to the nearest hundred."

"The pink car's price rounds to the same number when rounded to the nearest ten or nearest hundred."

"The gold car's price rounds down to the nearest ten, hundred and thousand."

"The green car's price rounds to £20 000 to the nearest ten thousand."

Stick the correct price from the sticker sheet on the windscreen of each car.

Answers on page 32

Negative numbers

Sapna has been learning about the temperatures in different cities around the world. Can you help her to find the difference in temperatures between each pair of cities?

City	Temperature
Toronto	-7°C
London	13°C
Moscow	-18°C
Rio	28°C

Toronto and **London**   The difference is: ....

Toronto and **Moscow**   The difference is: ....

London and **Moscow**   The difference is: ....

Moscow and **Rio**   The difference is: ....

Toronto and **Rio**   The difference is: ....

Sapna notices that the temperature in Warsaw drops by 10 degrees every month: 29°C, 19°C, 9°C...

She continues the sequence to estimate what the temperature will be in two more months if the pattern continues.

29°C, 19°C, 9°C, -9°C, -19°C

Can you explain and correct Sapna's mistake?

....

....

Answers on page 32

Order of operations

Lilia is collecting eggs on her parents' farm. She puts 2 eggs in a pan for lunch and fills 5 boxes of 6 eggs to sell. She writes this as 2 + 6 × 5 and asks her brother to work out how many she has collected in total. He says it's 40 eggs but Lilia isn't sure. She thinks it's 32 eggs. Who is correct and why?

....

....

The next day, Lilia collects 41 eggs and puts them in 3 boxes of 12. Which of these calculations shows how many eggs she has left?

$$12 \times 3 - 41 \qquad\qquad 41 - 12 \div 3$$

$$41 - 12 \times 3 \qquad\qquad 41 \div 12 - 3$$

These are the calculations Lilia writes for the eggs she collects on the remaining five days of the week. Circle the calculations she has done correctly according to BIDMAS. What should each answer have been?

$$3 + 8 \times 4 = 44$$

$$52 - 4 \times 5 = 32$$

$$60 + 12 \div 6 = 12$$

$$12 \times 5 - 3 = 24$$

$$30 - 4 \times 6 = 6$$

....

....

....

....

....

Answers on page 32

PARENT TIP: The rule of **BIDMAS** helps us work out the answer to a multi-step calculation by following the order: Brackets Indices Division Multiplication Addition Subtraction. Throw a dice three times. Using the numbers in any order, how many different answers can your child make using the rules of BIDMAS?

Factors and multiples

Bobby and Georgina are at the skate park on neighbouring ramps. Bobby stops for a rest at the top of the ramp after every 3 half pipes. Georgina stops after every 4 half pipes.

After how many half pipes will they both stop at the same time for the first time?

....

When will be the next three times that both of them will stop for a rest together?

....

Will they both stop together after 130 half pipes? How do you know?

....

....

Josh and Charlotte arrive at the skate park. They set off together but stop to rest at different times. They both stop for a rest together after 18 half pipes and then again after 36. After how many half pipes were they stopping to rest?

....

Bobby has brought 17 sweets with him that he wants to share but can't seem to divide them equally with his friends. Can you explain to Bobby why it isn't possible to share his sweets equally with anyone?

....

....

Can you think of three other numbers of sweets, less than 30, which can't be shared equally? ....

Answers on page 32

PARENT TIP: Play Times Tables Aerobics with your child. Pick two or more times tables and choose an action to represent multiples of each number, e.g. raise right arm for multiples of 3, or jump for multiples of 4. Count aloud from 1 and perform the actions when you say a multiple of the chosen times tables. How high can you count before you make a mistake?

Calculating mentally

Miss Appleby's class is having a maths quiz. The children must solve each calculation mentally with jottings. Alfie has done one question from each round. Use his examples to help you solve the other calculations.

Round 1
Rounding and adjusting

Alfie's workings out:
$234 + 19 = 234 + 20 - 1 = 253$

1. £13.46 + £2.99

....

2. 4650 − 1990

....

Round 2
Double one number and halve the other

Alfie's workings out:
$13 \times 4 = 26 \times 2 = 52$

1. 18 × 5

....

2. 24 × 6

....

Round 3
Factorising and reordering

Alfie's workings out:
$14 \times 12 = 7 \times 2 \times 12 = 84 \times 2 = 168$

1. 16 × 5

....

2. 24 × 8

....

Answers on page 32

PARENT TIP: Encourage your child to calculate mentally before using a written method. Ask them to consider: Can I use doubling or halving? Can I use the times tables that I know? Can I round the number and adjust the answer? Your child's recall of number bonds is crucial to their ability to calculate mentally.

8

Round 4
Partitioning and recombining

Alfie's workings out:
$18 \times 3 = 10 \times 3 + 8 \times 3 = 30 + 24 = 54$

1. 23×5

2. 17×6

....

3. 32×7

4. 26×8

....

Round 5
Using known facts

Alfie's workings out:
$3.2 \div 4 = 0.8$ because $32 \div 4 = 8$

1. 1.2×3

2. $6.3 \div 9$

....

3. $540 \div 6$

4. $280 \div 7$

....

Answers on page 32

9

Multiplying: written methods

The Mathemagical Theme Park has a different ticket price each day depending on how busy it expects to be. These are the admission numbers and ticket prices for each day of half term.

day	ticket price	admissions
Monday	£24	236
Tuesday	£18	304
Wednesday	£21	187
Thursday	£29	245
Friday	£32	453

Can you work out the total money taken for tickets each day? The first one is done for you.

Monday	**Tuesday**	**Wednesday**	**Thursday**	**Friday**
236	304	187	245	453
× 24	× 18	× 21	× 29	× 32
944				
+ 4720				
£5664				

ⓐ Which day made the most money? ....

ⓑ **Here is the calculation for Saturday's admissions. Can you write the missing numbers?**

Saturday

```
    5 ⦾ 3
  ×   ⦾ 5
  2 7 1 ⦾
+ ⦾ 6 2 9 0
  £1 ⦾ 0 ⦾ 5
```

ⓒ **The manager has worked out the takings for Sunday but has made a mistake. Can you explain it?**

....
....

Sunday

```
    628
  ×  38
   5024
+  1884
  £6908
```

Answers on page 32

Multiplying decimals

(a) A group of friends stop at a café for lunch. 3 of them decide to get pizza which costs £7.85 each and the other 5 have burgers at £5.49 each. What do they spend more on, pizza or burgers?

pizza

$$\begin{array}{r} 7.85 \\ \times \quad 3 \\ \hline \end{array}$$

£

burgers

$$\begin{array}{r} 5.49 \\ \times \quad 5 \\ \hline \end{array}$$

£

(b) The 8 friends each order a fizzy drink which is 0.85 litres. How much does the waitress pour out in total?

fizzy drinks

$$\begin{array}{r} 0.85 \\ \times \quad 8 \\ \hline \end{array}$$

litres

(c) The café has some delicious brownies. Each brownie is 12.5cm long and there are 7 brownies left. How long are they in total?

brownies

$$\begin{array}{r} 12.5 \\ \times \quad 7 \\ \hline \end{array}$$

cm

Answers on page 32

PARENT TIP: Give your child five random digits, e.g. 2, 3, 5, 7, 8. They need to use them to make a 3-digit number and a 2-digit number to multiply, e.g. 537 × 82. What is the largest product they can make? What's the smallest? Repeat with a decimal number with up to two places multiplied by a single digit, e.g. 23.57 × 8.

11

Dividing: written methods

At the Arty Electronics factory, video game consoles are being packed into boxes, ready to send to the shops. The iBot is packed in boxes of 15, the SpaceBlast in boxes of 24 and the Gamezone in boxes of 32.

This week, 3845 iBots, 6196 SpaceBlasts and 4272 Gamezones were made.

How many boxes will be filled with each video game console and how many of each will be left unboxed?

$$15\overline{)3845}$$

$$24\overline{)6196}$$

$$32\overline{)4272}$$

iBots left
unboxed

SpaceBlasts left
unboxed

Gamezones left
unboxed

....

....

....

The following week, Rory, one of the factory workers, has worked out that he will need 124 boxes for 1876 iBots. What mistake has he made?

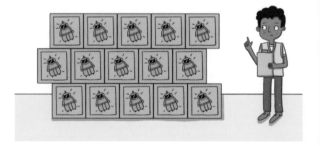

Rory's workings out:

$$15\overline{)18\overset{3}{7}\overset{7}{6}} 124 \ r16$$

....

....

....

....

....

Answers on page 32

939 SpaceBlasts were sold in the last 7 days. How many is that each day? Round your answer to one decimal place.

$$7 \sqrt{939}$$

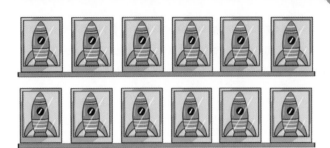

The special offer shelf is 195cm long. 6 Gamezones fit side by side on the shelf. How long is the Gamezone's box?

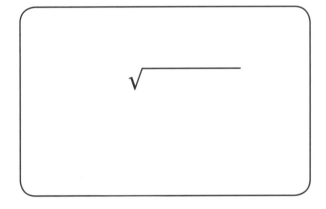

Two rival shops sold the Gamezone at different prices. Game World sold 25 for a total of £5990 and Gaming First sold 16 for a total of £4020. Which shop sold the Gamezone console for the highest price?

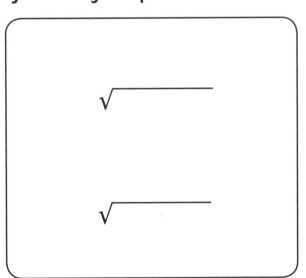

In one shop, 28 iBots were sold in the first week, making a total of £5313. How much did each one sell for?

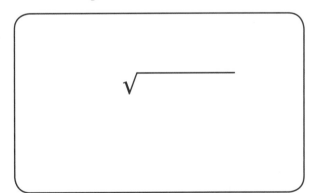

Answers on page 32

PARENT TIP: Encourage your child to make a list of multiples of the number they are dividing by at the side of the calculation. Counting aloud in multiples of numbers they are less familiar with will help with this, e.g. 23, 46, 69, 92. Try taking turns to count the different multiples.

Ordering fractions

After the Year 6 cake sale at school, there is enough cake left for a second cake sale. These are the fractions of each cake left over.

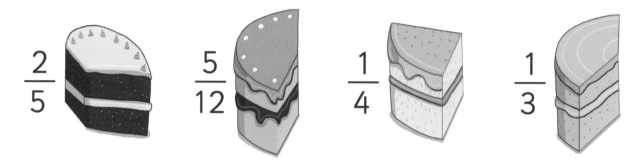

$\frac{2}{5}$

$\frac{5}{12}$

$\frac{1}{4}$

$\frac{1}{3}$

Using equivalent fractions, put the cake stickers from the sticker sheet in order of what is left, starting with the smallest fraction and ending with the biggest.

Mia's chocolate cake was cut into 12 pieces. There is less than $\frac{1}{2}$ but more than $\frac{1}{3}$ left at the end of the cake sale. Orla's toffee cake was cut into 8 pieces. There is more than $\frac{1}{2}$ but less than $\frac{3}{4}$ left. Use the stickers on your sticker sheet and stick in the fraction of each girl's cake that is left.

Mia's
chocolate cake

Orla's
toffee cake

Mia says they have the same amount of cake left, but Orla disagrees. Who is correct and why?

....

....

....

14

Answers on page 32

Adding and subtracting fractions

Some children brought the same types of cakes, so the next day, Mr Nelson combines these cakes together for the second cake sale.

Joe's mum made two carrot cakes for the sale. One was cut into 10 equal pieces and the other into 8. There are 3 pieces of each cake left for the second sale. What fraction is left altogether?

$$\frac{3}{10} + \frac{3}{8} =$$

There were $2\frac{1}{2}$ chocolate cakes at the first cake sale. At the end of the sale only $\frac{4}{5}$ of one cake is left. What fraction was sold?

Ethan made three Victoria sponge cakes with his dad for the first sale. At the end, $\frac{1}{4}$, $\frac{2}{3}$ and $\frac{3}{8}$ of the cakes are left. How much is there altogether for the second sale?

Answers on page 32

15

Multiplying fractions

Dan is the project manager of a new house that is being built. This is how the plot of land will be divided up:

house: $\frac{3}{5}$ garden: $\frac{1}{4}$ driveway: $\frac{1}{10}$ garage: $\frac{1}{20}$

Dan does some calculations to work out the fraction of the whole site that different features will take up. Can you help him find the answers?

The lounge is $\frac{1}{4}$ of the house.

$$\frac{1}{4} \times \frac{3}{5} =$$

The shed is $\frac{1}{8}$ of the garden.

$$\frac{1}{8} \times \frac{1}{4} =$$

Dan has got dirt on one of his calculations. Place the missing numbers 3, 5, 6 and 10 in the correct places in the calculation:

$$\frac{\square}{4} \times \frac{2}{\square} = \frac{\square}{20} = \frac{3}{\square}$$

The builders are ready to start building the house. $\frac{1}{3}$ of the bricks have been delivered, but $\frac{1}{2}$ of them are damaged. What fraction of the total bricks are ready for the builders to use?

....

....

$\frac{3}{5}$ of the doors need to be fitted by the end of the day. Nisha the joiner has to fit $\frac{3}{4}$ of them. What fraction of all the doors will she fit?

....

....

16

Answers on page 32

Dividing fractions

Dan has asked the tilers to start work on the kitchen. $\frac{2}{5}$ of the tiles are patterned. These will be split equally between the windowsill and sink. What fraction of the tiles will be used on the windowsill?

$$\frac{2}{5} \div 2 =$$

Can you help Dan to work out how much of each of these other materials to put in each room?

$\frac{2}{3}$ of all the timber is needed to build identical wardrobes in the 4 bedrooms. What fraction of all the timber should go in each room?

....

....

$\frac{1}{5}$ of the bags of plaster will be used in the 2 bathrooms. What fraction of the bags should Dan take to each bathroom?

....

....

$\frac{3}{8}$ of the insulation panels will be used in the 6 rooms upstairs. What fraction of the panels should be taken to each room?

....

....

Answers on page 32

PARENT TIP: Throw a dice four times to make the numerators and the denominators of two proper fractions, e.g. $\frac{2}{5}$ and $\frac{1}{2}$. Take turns to find their product. Who can make the largest fraction each time?

Fractions, decimals, percentages

Three sales assistants in a department store are putting sale tickets on some clothes. They do it in three different ways.

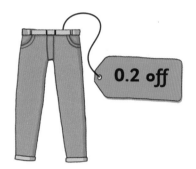 0.2 off

15% off

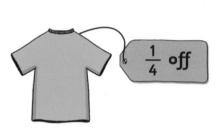 $\frac{1}{4}$ off

Which item of clothing has the most off? Explain why.

....

....

Match the sales tickets that show the same discount.
One has been done for you.

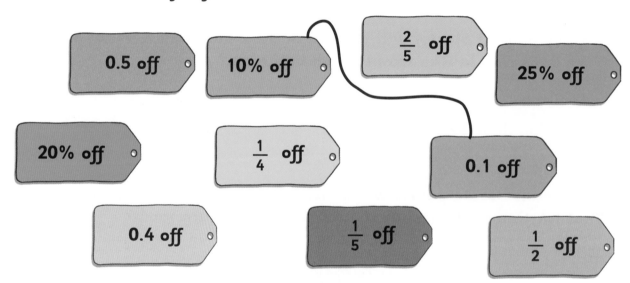

Anna has written all her sales tickets as percentages but Matt tells her to change them to fractions in their simplest form. Can you help?

15% off = ▢   75% off = ▢

60% off = ▢

Answers on page 32

Percentages

Pacha and his mum are in the sportswear department, choosing a new football kit. Calculate the savings on these football shirts.

£30
20% off
Saving of ....

£42
30% off
Saving of ....

£28
15% off
Saving of ....

A pair of football boots has 40% off. Pacha says he has two different ways to calculate this.

Method 1: find 10% and multiple by 4.

Method 2: find 50% and subtract 10%.

a) £24 ....

b) £60 ....

c) £80 ....

Which method do you prefer?

....

....

Pacha wants a pair of boots that cost £60 but today there's 30% off.
He says, "You just divide by 3 so the saving is £20."
His mum disagrees. Can you explain to him why he is wrong?

....

....

Answers on page 32

PARENT TIP: Play Would You Rather? with your child. Give your child real amounts to choose between, e.g. would you rather have 20% of 40 minutes on your tablet or 25% of 60 minutes? Would you rather have 30% of 20 grapes or 90% of 10 grapes?

19

Ratios

These are the numbers of different animals that came into the vet's surgery on Monday.

type of animal	number
dogs	12
cats	8
rabbits	3
hamsters	4
snakes	1
birds	2

Write these ratios in their simplest form.

dogs : hamsters ....

cats : birds ....

snakes : rabbits ....

These are the ratios of animals that came to see the vet on Tuesday.

cats : rabbits	dogs : rabbits	dogs : hamsters
5 : 1	4 : 1	3 : 2

The vet treated 15 cats. Complete this table to show how many of each animal was treated.

type of animal	number treated
dogs	
cats	15
rabbits	
hamsters	

Answers on page 32

On Wednesday, the vet saw 2 dogs for every 1 cat that came in for treatment. The vet treated 6 cats. How many dogs did she see?

....

....

Snakes and rabbits were brought in on Friday in the ratio of 1 snake for every 3 rabbits. There were 9 rabbits. How many snakes were brought in?

....

....

On Saturday, rabbits, hamsters and birds came to see the vet in the ratio 3:2:1. There were 24 rabbits, hamsters and birds in total. How many of each animal was there?

....

....

On Saturday and Sunday, the vet examined dogs in the ratio 2:3. If she examined 8 dogs on Saturday, how many did she examine on Sunday?

....

....

The vet saw 15 cats on Saturday and 18 cats on Sunday. She says the ratio of cats on Saturday compared to Sunday was 6:5. Is she right?

....

....

Answers on page 32

21

Algebra

Cooper is the manager at the mobile phone shop and has given his employees a formula for working out how much customers will pay each month (c) for each different tariff based on how much data (d) they use.

Can you write out the formula for each phone tariff? The first formula has been done for you.

tariff 1 | £25 per month plus £3 per GB of data

$$c = 25 + 3d$$

tariff 2 | £34 per month plus £2 per GB of data

....

tariff 3 | £21 per month plus £5 per GB of data

....

tariff 4 | £32 per month plus £1.50 per GB of data

....

Emma uses 3GB of data every month. Which is the cheapest tariff for Emma?

....

Using the stickers on the sticker sheet, match each of Emma's friends to the phone tariff that would be cheapest for them.

Ellie uses 10GB of data

Zoe uses 6GB of data

Tabby uses 1GB of data

22

Answers on page 32

These phones have different tariffs for customers who want to pay as they go for calls (m) and texts (t) only.

Write a formula for each phone tariff. The first one is done for you.

Mobile 1

50p per minute plus 3p per text

$c = 50m + 3t$

Mobile 2

20p per minute plus 5p per text

....

Mobile 3

10p per minute plus 20p per text

....

Mobile 4

30p per minute plus 10p per text

....

Sid is helping his grandmother choose a phone. He estimates that she will use about 300 minutes and 100 texts a month. Which phone should she buy and how much would she pay?

....

....

At the end of the first month, Sid's grandmother actually used about 200 minutes and 200 texts. Did they make the right decision and why?

....

....

Answers on page 32

PARENT TIP: Make solving equations fun! Give your child an equation, e.g. 2n + 3. Write the numbers from 0–9 with a pen on an inflatable ball and take turns to throw it back and forth. Whichever number your right thumb lands near becomes the value for n. Put this value into the equation and work out the answer.

Shape

Sinead loves making presents for her friends. She has built these gift boxes from nets she printed out from the internet. Can you match the net sticker from the sticker sheet to the gift box it made?

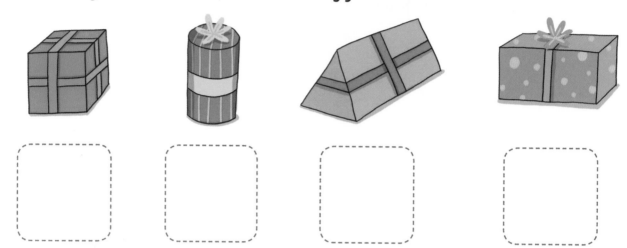

She needs to make a hexagonal prism shaped box for another gift but can't find a net on the internet. She knows it will need hexagonal and rectangular faces. Can you work out how many it will need of each?

hexagonal faces: rectangular faces:

What shapes and how many of each will she need for a pentagonal-based pyramid box?

....

....

Can you draw the net for her in this space?

Answers on page 32

Sinead has been learning about shapes in school and decides to impress her little brother with her 'psychic' powers! She prints off some shapes from the internet. Then she asks him to measure just one angle with his protractor and tells him that she can guess the rest of the shape's angles!

Sinead uses her knowledge of shapes and these two rules:

Angles of a triangle add up to 180°
Angles of a quadrilateral add up to 360°

These are the angles her brother measures on each shape:
Fill in the missing angles that Sinead gives her brother for each shape.

equilateral triangle	isosceles triangle	isosceles trapezium	rhombus
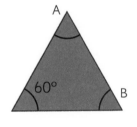	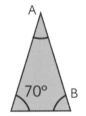	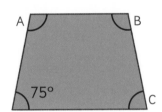	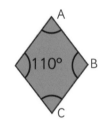

equilateral triangle

A ....
B ....

isosceles triangle

A ....
B ....

isosceles trapezium

A ....
B ....
C ....

rhombus

A ....
B ....
C ....

Sinead's dad shows her a rule for the internal angles of regular polygons. He says, "Divide 360° by the number of vertices and subtract that amount from 180°."

Can you use his rule to work out the internal angles of a regular decagon (10-sided shape)?

....

....

Answers on page 32

PARENT TIP: Play My Secret Shape with your child. Take turns to describe a shape using its properties and ask each other to guess it. Use properties, such as lines of symmetry, number of equal sides, angles, 2D or 3D, etc. Also use the angle rules for triangles and quadrilaterals, and ask your child to guess the missing angles in your secret shape.

Converting measures

John and his family are travelling around America during the summer holidays. John has been learning about converting measures in school, so he looks out for measures he can convert along the way.

John keeps track of how far they have driven. How many metres have they travelled each day?

day of the week	distance in km	distance in m
Monday	31.4km	
Tuesday	50.25km	
Wednesday	76.06km	
Thursday	100.5km	
Friday	84.453km	

His dad tells him they have travelled 73 240 metres since they set off this morning. How many kilometres have they travelled so far?

....

Tomorrow they have two journeys of 205 320m and 46.3km to make. How far will they travel in total?

....

They weigh their luggage to make sure it isn't too heavy for the plane flight home. The scale shows 18 450g. Their allowance is 20kg. Are they within the allowance? How do you know?

....

At the gas station, they buy 4 drinks that measure 650ml each. How many litres do the drinks add up to in total?

....

Answers on page 32

John's dad normally measures the distance they travel in miles.
John helps him convert the distances from km to miles using this rule:

5 miles = 8 km

Can you use John's rule to match the distances below?

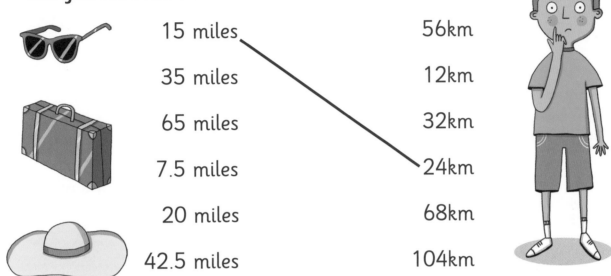

15 miles	56km
35 miles	12km
65 miles	32km
7.5 miles	24km
20 miles	68km
42.5 miles	104km

John's dad says that 1 mile is about 1.6km. Use this rule to complete the boxes with one of these symbols from the sticker sheet:

< > =

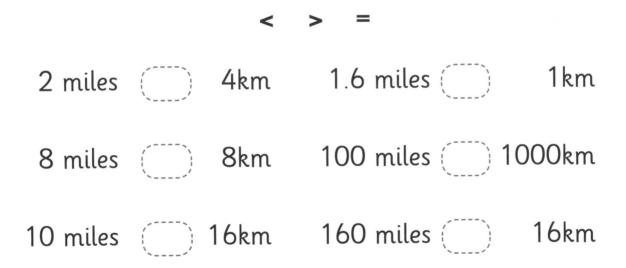

2 miles	◯	4km		1.6 miles	◯	1km
8 miles	◯	8km		100 miles	◯	1000km
10 miles	◯	16km		160 miles	◯	16km

Answers on page 32

PARENT TIP: Whenever you drive somewhere, encourage your child to work out the approximate distance in kilometres by using the conversion 5 miles = 8 kilometres. Also you can ask them to use both metric and imperial measures in everyday life, e.g. when you are cooking and the recipe needs 75g of rice, ask your child what it is in kg?

Area and perimeter

Neighbours Kate and Alice are racing each other on their scooters around the outside of their rectangular gardens.

Kate says, "It's not fair because our gardens are different sizes so we won't travel the same distance."

They measure the perimeters to check and are surprised that both perimeters are 44m. What could the length and width of each garden be if they are both whole numbers?

One possibility is 4m by 18m because (4 + 18) × 2 = 44. How many other answers can you find? (Hint: there are 11 possibilities.)

....

....

....

....

....

Alice says, "The difference between the areas of our gardens is 35m²." What are the measurements of each garden? (Hint: find all possible areas and work out which two have a difference of 35m².)

....

....

....

Answers on page 32

PARENT TIP: Let your child measure the length and width of different rooms and spaces around your home. Which room has the biggest/smallest area? Which has the biggest/smallest perimeter? Is it the same room? Can your child draw another room with the same area but a different perimeter?

In school the next day, Kate and Alice are learning about the area of triangles. Their teacher shows them that if they draw a diagonal across a rectangle they can make two triangles with half the area of the rectangle.

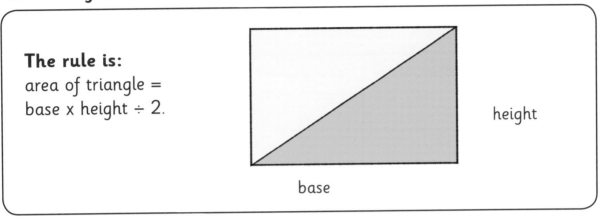

The rule is:
area of triangle = base x height ÷ 2.

height

base

Can you use the rule to find the area of these triangles?

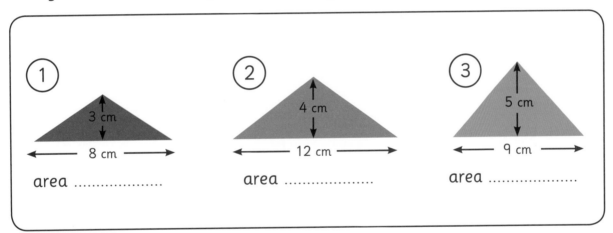

① 3 cm
8 cm
area ....

② 4 cm
12 cm
area ....

③ 5 cm
9 cm
area ....

What are the missing base and height measurements in these triangles?

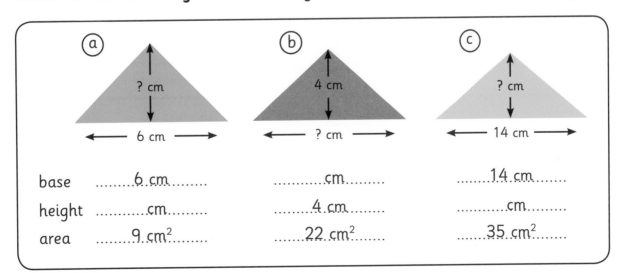

ⓐ ? cm
6 cm

ⓑ 4 cm
? cm

ⓒ ? cm
14 cm

	ⓐ	ⓑ	ⓒ
base	6 cm	.... cm	14 cm
height	.... cm	4 cm	.... cm ....
area	9 cm²	22 cm²	35 cm²

Answers on page 32

Mean

On Millie's street, the neighbours have been competing to find out who can recycle the most waste. They have kept a record of all the items in their recycling bins over the last few weeks. This is Millie's record:

	plastic bottles	newspapers	tin cans	glass jars
week one	4	2	7	2
week two	6	1	5	4
week three	3	3	9	3
week four	5	4	12	5

Calculate the mean number of each item over the last 4 weeks.

plastic bottles

$(4 + 6 + 3 + 5) \div 4 =$

....

newspapers

tin cans

....

....

glass jars

....

....

Tilly next door only recorded her recycling over the last 3 weeks. Can you complete the missing numbers in her table?

	plastic bottles	newspapers	tin cans	glass jars
week one	4		4	10
week two	5	2		11
week three		5	8	
mean	**4**	**3**	**7**	**9**

Answers on page 32

The neighbours compare the number of glass jars they have each recycled. There are 6 houses taking part and they recycled a total of 42 jars. What is the mean number of jars per household?

....

....

Only 3 households recycled tin cans. If their mean number of cans was 6, how many cans did they recycle in total?

....

....

In the last week, only 4 households recycled newspapers. Their mean number of newspapers was 3. If the first 2 households recycled 4 each, how many did the other 2 households recycle?

....

....

The mean number of plastic bottles for 5 households was 4. When the sixth house brings their bottles, the mean increases by 2. How many bottles did the sixth house add to the recycling?

....

....

....

Answers on page 32

PARENT TIP: To find the mean, we add the individual numbers and divide the total by the amount of numbers, e.g. 3 + 6 + 8 + 9 = 26. There are 4 numbers so 26 ÷ 4 = 6.5. Use everyday life situations to help your child practise finding the mean, e.g. you could ask them to work out the mean number of sweets in several paper bags.

Answers

Page 2: Big numbers

Kinsman	Finch	Randles	Hagarth
£8 098 324	£ 8 235 938	£14 568 400	£15 408 276

player name	wage change	new wages
Randles	£600 000 decrease	£13 968 400
Finch	£70 000 increase	£8 305 938
Kinsman	£450 000 increase	£8 548 324
Hagarth	£9000 decrease	£15 399 276

digits 1 & 2	£2 321 450	<	£2 323 640
digits 2 & 2	£2 322 450	<	£2 323 640
digits 3 & 2	£2 323 450	<	£2 323 640
digits 4 and above & 3 and above	£2 324 450	<	£2 333 640

Page 3: Decimal numbers

No, Robbie is wrong. James should say, "4 tenths is larger than 1 tenth so the rest of the digits don't matter."

William is wrong. 14 003m ÷ 1000 = 14.003km

Robbie: 12.042km   Jenny: 9.802km   William: 10.46km

Poppy: 15.8km   Connor: 8.045km

13.4km × 1000 = 13 400m   3400cm ÷ 100 = 34m

Page 4: Rounding numbers

The black car: £12 549 rounds up to £13 000.

Kyle's dad will pay £15 000.

It is the same price: £15 000.

Page 5: Negative numbers

Toronto and London: 20°C

Toronto and Moscow: 11°C

London and Moscow: 31°C

Moscow and Rio: 46°C

Toronto and Rio: 35°C

From 9°C to -9°C is a difference of 18°C. It should be 29°C, 19°C, 9°C, -1°C, -11°C

Page 6: Order of operations

Lilia is correct. Multiplication comes before addition: (6 × 5) + 2 = 30 + 2 = 32

41 – 12 × 3. Lilia has 5 eggs left.

3 + 8 × 4 = 44 is wrong, the correct answer is 35.

52 × 4 × 5 = 32 is correct.

60 + 12 ÷ 6 = 12 is wrong, the correct answer is 62.

12 × 5 × 3 = 24 is wrong, the correct answer is 57.

30 – 4 × 6 = 6 is correct.

Page 7: Factors and multiples

12 half pipes.

24, 36 and 48 half pipes.

No. 130 isn't a multiple of 12.

They were stopping at 2 and 9 half pipes, or 3 and 6 half pipes.

17 is a prime number and prime numbers can only be divided by itself and 1.

2, 3, 5, 7, 11,13,19, 23, 29 are all prime numbers below 30.

Pages 8–9: Calculating mentally

Round 1:

1. £13.46 + £2.99 = £13.46 + £3 – £0.01 = £16.45

2. 4650 – 1990 = 4650 – 2000 + 10 = 2660

Round 2:

1. 18 × 5 = 9 × 10 = 90

2. 24 × 6 = 12 × 12 = 144

Round 3:

1. 16 × 5 = 4 × 4 × 5 = 4 × 20 = 80

2. 24 × 8 = 12 × 2 × 8 = 96 × 2 = 192

Round 4:

1. 23 × 5 = 20 × 5 + 3 × 5 = 100 + 15 = 115

2. 17 × 6 = 10 × 6 + 7 × 6 = 60 + 42 = 102

3. 32 × 7 = 30 × 7 + 2 × 7 = 210 + 14 = 224

4. 26 × 8 = 20 × 8 + 6 × 8 = 160 + 48 = 208

Round 5:

1. 1.2 × 3 = 3.6 because 12 × 3 = 36

2. 6.3 ÷ 9 = 0.7 because 63 ÷ 9 = 7

3. 540 ÷ 6 = 90 because 54 ÷ 6 = 9

4. 280 ÷ 7 = 40 because 28 ÷ 7 = 4

Page 10: Multiplying: written methods

a. Friday made the most money.

Monday	Tuesday	Wednesday	Thursday	Friday	**b.** Saturday
236	304	187	245	453	543
× 24	× 18	× 21	× 29	× 32	× 35
944	2432	187	2205	906	2715
+ 4720	+ 3040	+ 3740	+ 4900	+ 13 590	+ 16 290
£5664	£5472	£3927	£7105	£14 496	£19 005

c. The manager has forgotten to use a place holder when multiplying by 30.

Page 11: Multiplying decimals

a. The friends spend more on burgers.

b. The waitress pours 6.8 litres in total.

c. The brownies are 87.5cm long.

Pages 12–13: Dividing: written methods

The iBots fill 256 boxes with 5 left unboxed. The SpaceBlasts fill 258 boxes with 4 left unboxed. The Gamezones fill 133 boxes with 16 left unboxed. The answer 125 r1, not 124 r16. You cannot have a remainder of 16 when dividing by 15.

134.1 SpaceBlasts were sold each day.

The Gamezone's box is 32.5cm long.

Gaming First sold the Gamezone at the higher price.

The iBots sold for £189.75 each.

Page 14: Ordering fractions

Mia $\frac{5}{12}$ Orla $\frac{5}{8}$

Orla is correct because even though they both have 5 pieces left, her eighths are bigger than Mia's twelfths.

Page 15: Adding and subtracting fractions

Carrot cakes: $\frac{27}{40}$. Chocolate cakes:$1\frac{7}{10}$. Victoria sponge cakes: $1\frac{7}{24}$.

Page 16: Multiplying fractions

Lounge: $\frac{3}{20}$. Shed: $\frac{1}{32}$. $\frac{3}{4} \times \frac{2}{5} = \frac{6}{20} = \frac{3}{10}$

Bricks: $\frac{1}{6}$. Doors: $\frac{9}{20}$.

Page 17: Dividing fractions

Tiles: $\frac{1}{5}$. Timber: $\frac{1}{6}$. Bags of plaster: $\frac{1}{10}$. Insulation panels: $\frac{1}{16}$.

Page 18: Fractions, decimals, percentages

$\frac{1}{4}$ off is best because it is the same as 0.25 (more than 0.2), or 25% (more than 15%).

15% = $\frac{15}{100}$ = $\frac{3}{20}$.   75% = $\frac{3}{4}$.   60% = $\frac{3}{5}$.

Page 19: Percentages

Shirt 1: £30 – 20% off saving of £6   **Shirt 2:** £42 – 30% off saving of £12.60

Shirt 3: £28 – 15% off saving of £4.20

a. method 1: £2.40 × 4 = £9.60   method 2: £12 – £2.40 = £9.60

b. method 1: £6 × 4 = £24   method 2: £30 – £6 = £24

c. method 1: £8 × 4 = £32   method 2: £40 – £8 = £32

30% is 3 × 10%, which is 3 × £6, so £18. Dividing by 3 would be finding $\frac{1}{3}$ which is the same as 33.333...%, not 30%.

Pages 20–21: Ratios

dogs : hamsters = 3:1   cats : birds = 4:1   snakes : rabbits = 1:3

type of animal	number treated
dogs	12
cats	15
rabbits	3
hamsters	8

12 dogs. 3 snakes. 12 rabbits, 8 hamsters and 4 birds. 12 dogs. No, the ratio is 5:6.

Pages 22–23: Algebra

1. [c = 25 + 3d]   **2.** [c = 34 + 2d]   **3.** [c = 21 + 5d]   **4.** [c = 32 + 1.5d]

Mobile tariff 1 is the cheapest for Emma.

Mobile tariff 4 is cheapest for Ellie and Zoe. Mobile tariff 3 is cheapest for Tabby.

1. [c = 50m + 3t]   **2.** [c = 20m + 5t]   **3.** [c = 10m + 20t]   **4.** [c = 30m + 10t]

Sid's grandmother should buy mobile 3 and would pay £50.

No, they should have bought mobile 2, it would have been £10 cheaper.

Pages 24–25: Shape

2 hexagonal faces and 6 rectangular faces.

1 pentagonal face and 5 triangular faces.

Pentagonal-based pyramid box net:

Equilateral triangle	60° and 60°	
Isosceles triangle	70° and 40°	
Isosceles trapezium	75°, 105° and 105°	
Rhombus	110°, 70° and 70°	

Decagon internal angle: 180 – (360 ÷ 10) = 144°

Pages 26–27: Converting measures

day of the week	distance in km	distance in m
Monday	31.4km	31 400m
Tuesday	50.25km	50 250m
Wednesday	76.06km	76 060m
Thursday	100.5km	100 500m
Friday	84.453km	84 453m

73.24km. 251.62km (or 251 620m). Yes, 18 450g = 18.45kg. 2.6 litres in total.

[15 miles = 24km   35 miles = 56km   65 miles = 104km   7.5 miles = 12km

20 miles = 32km   42.5 miles = 68km]

2 miles < 4km   1.6 miles > 1km

8 miles > 8km   100 miles < 1000km

10 miles = 16km   160 miles > 16km

Pages 28–29: Area and perimeter

1m by 21m   2m by 20m   3m by 19m   4m by 18m   5m by 17m

6m by 16m   7m by 15m   8m by 14m   9m by 13m   10m by 12m

11m by 11m.

The two gardens must be 5m × 17m = 85m² and 10m × 12m = 120m²

because 120m² – 85m² = 35m²

Triangle 1	8 × 3 ÷ 2 = 12cm²
Triangle 2	12 × 4 ÷ 2 = 24cm²
Triangle 3	9 × 5 ÷ 2 = 22.5cm²

Triangle a	Base = 6cm	Height = 3cm	Area = 9cm²
Triangle b	Base = 11cm	Height = 4cm	Area = 22cm²
Triangle c	Base = 14cm	Height = 5cm	Area = 35cm²

Pages 30–31: Mean

plastic bottles   (4 + 6 + 3 + 5) ÷ 4 = 4.5

newspapers   (2 + 1 + 3 + 4) ÷ 4 = 2.5

tin cans   (7 + 5 + 9 + 12) ÷ 4 = 8.25

glass jars   (2 + 4 + 3 + 5) ÷ 4 = 3.5

	plastic bottles	newspapers	tin cans	glass jars
week one	4	2	4	10
week two	5	2	9	11
week three	3	5	8	6
mean	**4**	**3**	**7**	**9**

7 jars per household. 18 cans in total. 4 between them (1+3 or 2+2). 16 bottles.